White Patch
A City Sparrow

written and illustrated by

Olive L. Earle

WILLIAM MORROW AND COMPANY
NEW YORK   1958

The little brown birds living in Battery
Park knew nothing of hills, woods, meadows,
and brooks. Their hills were skyscrapers of
steel and concrete. Their woods were rows
of trees and groups of shrubs. Their only
meadows were patches of grass enclosed
by iron railings, and their brooks were

the wide stretches of the harbor. The park was at the lower tip of Manhattan Island. The little birds were house, or English, sparrows. They seemed quite content to live in New York City.

One of the sparrows in the flock was only two months old. He looked different from the others, because he had a patch of white feathers—almost like an epaulet—on his left shoulder, and he was more fluffy than the older birds. They were about six and a·

quarter inches long. Except for his shorter tail, he was as big as they were.

White Patch's first home had been a nest on a ledge in the park's old circular fort, Castle Clinton. He wasn't in the least afraid of the people who walked in the park. He hopped fearlessly around their feet in the hope that some crumbs would be thrown to him. It was an easier way to get a meal than hunting for insects and seeds.

The pigeons who roosted on the buildings around the park also liked people. They, too, ate crumbs, but they preferred the cracked corn that was occasionally tossed to

them. The pigeons did not hop; they walked. They paraded along the paths, with one pink foot almost stepping on the other.

One damp Sunday morning the park was nearly deserted, and there were no free meals for the birds. Young White Patch hunted and hunted for something to eat. At last, under a bench, he found a bit of soggy doughnut. Pulling and tugging, he dragged it out. In an instant the other sparrows surrounded him, some flying and some hopping.

Squabbling excitedly, they all tried to snatch the prize. White Patch managed to hold on to a piece of it, and he gulped it down as fast as he could.

After his meal he flew to a railing and wiped his bill on it. A pigeon who had arrived too late for the doughnut feast sat near him for a few minutes. Then, with a clapping of her wings, she took off to join her companions, who were flying in wide circles over the park. Before she had time to catch up with the flock, disaster overtook her. Unseen by the birds in the park, a peregrine falcon far up in the sky had watched

their movements. He flew in spirals until he
was directly over the straggler. Then he
suddenly dropped like a stone, and seized
the pigeon in his strong talons. She had no

chance to escape, and he carried her off to the top of the skyscraper which he was using as a temporary home.

All the birds were frightened at the sight of the falcon. The flock of pigeons flew in confusion to the shelter of a building. The sparrows hid in a plane tree and huddled just as close to its trunk as they could get. Some starlings who were visiting the park took refuge in a clump of tall shrubs.

Fortunately the falcon moved on. Day after day the other birds flew around the park without being raided by another enemy from the sky.

The sparrows spent almost their entire time looking for food. A fountain supplied them with water, but its pool was too deep to be used as a bath. And since the well-paved walks were free of puddles, even after a heavy rain, the sparrows had to be content with dust baths. Each made his own bath and chased away any other bird that came near it.

With his breast, White Patch pressed
down the powdery soil near a bush, pushing
and turning until he had made a little hollow.
This was his bath, and he wallowed in it.
With outstretched wings, he threw dust
right over his back, so that it sifted through

his fluffed-out feathers. Then he preened; one by one, he drew his feathers through his bill to remove the dust and dirt. Perhaps this made him feel more comfortable, but he didn't look any cleaner than he had before.

All the city sparrows were so dirty that their color pattern was lost in grime. The dark streaks on White Patch's brown back and the hint of black on his light chest barely showed. His white shoulder patch was smutty. Except for his feet and bill, which were more pinkish than hers, he looked very much like his mother, who had a faintly striped brown back and light under parts.

The park pigeons were not much interested in bathing; but they, too, drank from the fountain pool. Ordinarily, when a bird drinks, it takes a quick sip, then raises its head and swallows the water that runs down its throat. But the pigeon and other birds of its family have a way of drinking that seems to be all their own. It dips in its bill as far as its nostrils and, without raising its head, draws the water into its throat in one long draft.

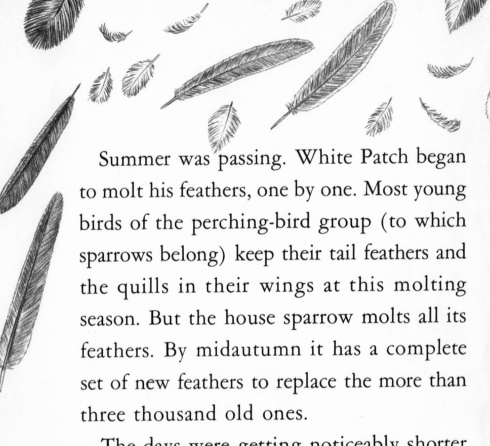

Summer was passing. White Patch began to molt his feathers, one by one. Most young birds of the perching-bird group (to which sparrows belong) keep their tail feathers and the quills in their wings at this molting season. But the house sparrow molts all its feathers. By midautumn it has a complete set of new feathers to replace the more than three thousand old ones.

The days were getting noticeably shorter now. At night the chief sounds were the hum of the city traffic and the tooting of boat whistles in the harbor. But high, high

in the sky there were hundreds of tiny, twittering birds. They were the first of many flocks of different kinds of birds that would travel south for the winter.

White Patch may have heard the travelers, but he did not join them; for house sparrows do not migrate. Although they may wander about, they stay in their home range all year long.

The ancestors of all the house sparrows in America made long journeys once upon

a time—but by boat. More than a hundred years ago, European sparrows (which actually are members of the weaver-finch family) were brought to this country from England. Over a period of time, groups of them were released here in the hope that they would increase in numbers and destroy insect pests. They did multiply; but they became a nuisance to farmers and gardeners, for they

destroyed useful insects as well as pests, and they also ate sprouting crops and ripened grain. Colonies of them thrived so well that they overflowed every district in which they settled. House sparrows are now found in populated areas all over the United States and in much of Canada. Many people do not like them, because they sometimes drive native birds away or take over the

nesting places of more attractive birds, such as bluebirds and house wrens. But in the cities, where other birds are scarce, people usually enjoy their cheerful twittering and trusting ways.

The Battery Park colony did not increase greatly, in spite of the many young ones that were hatched there. Some of them wandered to other parts of the city, and some of the baby birds were drowned in heavy rainstorms. And a few of them, less alert than the older birds, were caught by prowling cats. But White Patch survived these perils.

Together with other members of his family, he explored the park repeatedly. Then he grew more adventurous. One morning, all by himself, he followed two pigeons to a ferryboat that was about to leave for a trip across the harbor to Staten Island. Looking for possible crumbs, the pigeons lit on the deck. White Patch flew to the roof of a wheelhouse.

The ferryboat started its twenty-five-minute journey across the bay. A few minutes

later it drew near the old cannon-topped fort on Governor's Island, and the pigeons flew away. But White Patch stayed on his lofty perch. From it he could see gulls soaring, with an occasional flap of their long wings, behind the boat. He heard their mewing cries and watched them as they plunged downward, steering with feet and tail, to inspect something floating on the water.

The course of the ferryboat was marked by red buoys, the flashing light in the top of each one barely visible in the bright sunshine. As the waves rocked the buoys, swinging hammers struck their big bells and made them clang.

To starboard, Liberty held her torch high. Because of the action of the salt air, the copper of the towering statue had long ago become coated with a film of soft green.

Although Staten Island is a part of New York City, the towers of Manhattan seemed

far away by the time White Patch's boat reached its dock. Here, too, as in Battery Park, there were pigeons. Familiar, also, was the sight of a flock of starlings wheeling black against the sky.

White Patch flew from the boat and over the ferryhouse to an avenue of trees. There he looked for insects to eat, because he was hungry after his voyage. Then on he went, settling occasionally in an empty lot to pick up weed seeds. In true sparrow fashion, his flights were brief; and he always flew within easy reach of the shelter of a tree or a building.

At last he reached a large garden, with
thick shrubs and tall trees, and flew over
its high hedge. On the ground, in front of

an old house, he found a shallow pan of water. He hopped into it, took a drink, and then dipped in the water. He shook his feathers and dipped again. He shook and dipped again and again. When at last he

flew to a nearby bush, he was a much cleaner sparrow, but his bath water was much dirtier.

He preened the water from his feathers while he sat drying in the sun. Then he joined a group of house sparrows and white-throats that were feeding on the lawn beside the house. Juncos flew from place to place, each one flashing the white feathers that edged its tail. In a tree, a cardinal called to his mate, and overhead flew a family of screaming blue jays.

Unlike the tidy park, much of the garden was wild and overgrown. Tangled vines and thickets provided shelter for the birds at

night. White Patch slept in a dense shrub, crouching snugly on a twig. Because he had fourteen vertebrae in his flexible neck (we have only seven), he could twist his head with ease and bury his bill in the feathers of his back.

Many kinds of migrating birds stopped briefly to rest and feed in the garden. The

robins, the brown thrashers, and other summer residents left for the South; but White
Patch decided to make his home in the
garden. If no misfortune overtook him, he
might live here as long as twelve years.

Soon the winter coats of squirrels began

to gleam like silver, and their tails grew more bushy. Only occasionally, now, were the chirps of a cricket heard.

One chilly morning a sparrow hawk hovered over the lawn where the birds were feeding. The grasshoppers—his favorite food—had disappeared, and he hoped to satisfy his hunger with a meal of sparrow. As he was about to dive at the flock, White Patch saw him and gave the alarm. Even when he was busily occupied, he was always conscious of possible danger. Quickly he flew into a bush, and like a flash the other birds, without a sound, followed him to safety.

The trees lost their leaves as the garden prepared for its winter sleep. Food was harder for the birds to find, and it seemed as though they might not get enough to eat. But they did. Near the house was a rough wooden table and on it, one morning, White Patch found crumbs and all sorts of seeds, as well as the grit that birds need to help them digest their food.

The other sparrows saw White Patch pecking eagerly, and they joined him for a feast. They swallowed the tiniest seeds whole, but they split open the larger ones to get at

the kernel. Each sparrow's heavy bill, with a sharp cutting edge at its base, was a perfect tool for crushing a seed held in place by the sparrow's tongue.

New arrivals in the garden saw the sparrows feeding, so they came and joined them, to get a meal. The chickadees and nuthatches enjoyed the peanuts and also the chunks of suet that were wedged in branches. The woodpeckers liked the suet too.

The male cardinal acted as though he were the most important bird in the garden, often chasing the others away—especially his mate—when they came to feed.

Sunflower seeds were a favorite food of all the birds, but they were often too tough for the sparrows to open. The cardinal could open them easily, so White Patch would edge up to him and grab little pieces of kernel as they fell to the ground.

As real winter came, the water in the drinking pan froze over. Now the big blue jays were useful, because they were able to hammer a hole in the crust of ice with their sharp bills. One by one, the little birds sipped their drinks of water through the opening. When snow fell, and buried the pan, they ate mouthfuls of it. If the snow froze and had a hard surface, they waited near the house until fresh water was put out.

A January thaw made the house sparrows behave as though spring had really come. Although their song was tuneless, they did the best they could, chirping and twittering gaily. They hopped happily through the bushes, nipping the buds. Some even picked up bits of dry grass as though they were thinking of nest building.

Their cheerfulness didn't last long, though, for soon there came more icy weather and cold winds. All the birds sought shelter. White Patch crouched, like a little ball of feathers, in the most protected spot he could find. His fluffed-out feathers trapped the air warmed by his body, and this layer of warm air kept the cold from penetrating too easily. In such frigid weather, very little blood circulated in his feet and perhaps that was why they did not freeze.

Even when strong winds buffeted him, White Patch was able to hold on to his branch. Like all perching birds, he had very powerful muscles and tendons in his legs and toes. When he lit on a twig, a nerve center in the sole of each foot automatically tightened his grip. When he crouched, the position and weight of his body kept the tendons tightly drawn so that his toes actually locked around his perch.

One day the wind blew harder than ever. Hunger at last forced White Patch to leave the center of a dense bush in which he had taken shelter from the gale. He hopped toward the outer branches, bent on making his way to the food table. Ordinarily, he was very skillful in avoiding obstacles when he was flying from a perch, but this time his skill did not help him. The whole bush was thrashing in the wind, as if it might be torn apart at any moment; and just as White Patch fluttered through the branches, two of them whipped together, catching him and holding him fast. Although he struggled wildly he could not escape. The next

moment, though, another gust forced the branches apart, and he was free. He managed to make his way to the porch of the

house, where he squatted close to the wall until he had recovered from his fright. There were seeds on the floor, and soon he was pecking at them happily.

By the time the robins arrived, in mid-March, the house sparrows were getting ready to nest. Now the male cardinal whistled joyously and courted his mate, feeding her with choice seeds. The blue jays were bobbing and bowing in the tree-tops. The whole garden seemed to know

that winter was over and spring was here.

White Patch, like the other male sparrows, looked very handsome in his spring plumage. It was not new, but the gray tips that had veiled the rich color of his feathers had gradually worn away. His throat and bib were a rich black. The crown of his head was gray, bordered with chestnut-brown. His cheeks were white, and he had a white bar on each wing. His bill was black, instead of brownish; and, as usual, he kept it polished by rubbing it back and forth across a twig.

Although the females lacked the males'
strongly marked pattern, they looked less
drab than before. There was great activity
among the males, but the females did not
pay much attention to the scolding and
fighting that went on continuously. After
much bickering, White Patch claimed a

mate. He postured before her, with his head thrown back to show his black bib. Drooping his wings and spreading his tail in the air, he hopped up and down in one spot. Then he hopped around the female. At last she made a grab at his wing to show that she approved of him.

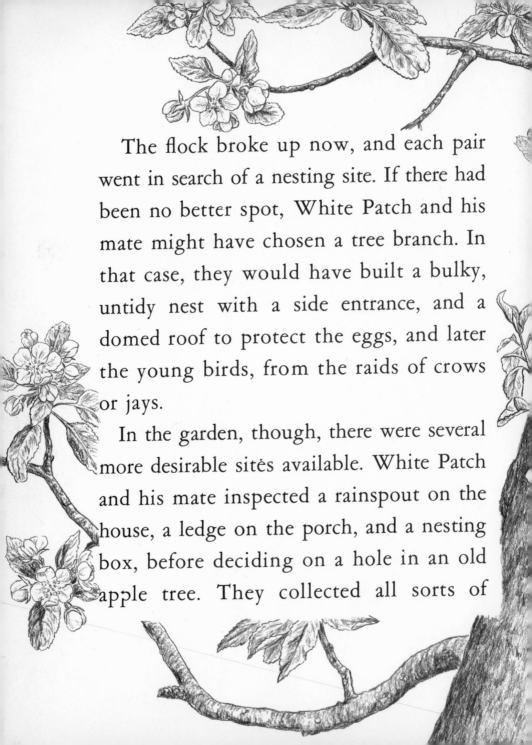

The flock broke up now, and each pair went in search of a nesting site. If there had been no better spot, White Patch and his mate might have chosen a tree branch. In that case, they would have built a bulky, untidy nest with a side entrance, and a domed roof to protect the eggs, and later the young birds, from the raids of crows or jays.

In the garden, though, there were several more desirable sites available. White Patch and his mate inspected a rainspout on the house, a ledge on the porch, and a nesting box, before deciding on a hole in an old apple tree. They collected all sorts of

material, until the hole was almost filled
with little twigs, dry grass, string, bits of
cloth and paper, and other trash. They used
feathers to line the nest.

At last they seemed satisfied with their mass of rubbish, and the female laid her eggs in it. She laid one each morning until there were five dull, grayish-white eggs, more or less evenly speckled with reddish-brown. The eggs of sparrows vary in color from plain white to dark brown.

After the set was complete, the female sat on the eggs to keep them warm. In preparation for this incubation period, she shed a patch of the soft feathers on her underside. This left a bare spot, making it possible for the warmth of her body to come in direct contact with the eggs. Later, feathers would grow again on this brood patch—as it is called.

Sometimes the female left the nest to hunt for food, but she always returned before the eggs had had time to chill. Before settling down again, she turned the eggs. Then she puffed out her breast feathers to make sure that the brood patch was over the eggs.

While his mate was sitting, White Patch showed very little interest in her or in the nest. Once in a while, though, he brought an extra piece of nesting material to the

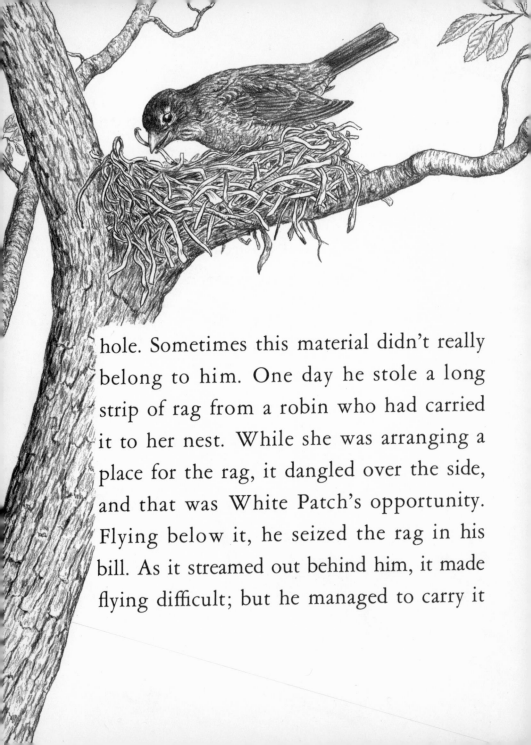

hole. Sometimes this material didn't really belong to him. One day he stole a long strip of rag from a robin who had carried it to her nest. While she was arranging a place for the rag, it dangled over the side, and that was White Patch's opportunity. Flying below it, he seized the rag in his bill. As it streamed out behind him, it made flying difficult; but he managed to carry it

to his own nest hole in the apple tree.

After being kept warm for twelve days,
the eggs began to hatch, From now on,
White Patch seemed to realize his respons-
ibilities, for he shared in the care of the
young birds.

Some birds, such as ducklings, come from the egg with their bodies covered with thick down. Baby robins and many other newly hatched birds have sparse patches of fluff. But when baby house sparrows peck their way out, they are absolutely naked.

For the first day or two after they hatched, the tiny pinkish babies had to be kept warm, so between feedings one of the parents brooded them. It was always their mother who covered them at night. White Patch took an occasional turn during the day. It was the female who kept the nest clean, by removing the little sacs of waste matter.

Both parents hunted food for their

young ones. For a few days the babies had food that had first been partly digested in the crop of one of their parents. For three or four days the huge eyes of the babies were tightly shut, but any sign of movement at the edge of the nest made each one open its gaping red-lined mouth.

By the fourth day of a baby sparrow's life, little dark dots show in definite tracts under its skin, making it look a grayish color. These dots are the beginnings of its feathers. By the seventh day they poke through the skin like little spikes. Many of them quickly break open and release the feathers inside. Three days later the little sparrow is well fledged and shows its color pattern.

By the time they were ten days old, White Patch's lively youngsters had grown so big that the nest was crowded with them. They jostled, they pushed, they stretched their wings as much as they could in their cramped quarters, and they cheeped noisily.

As the nestlings grew, they had a variety of food. It took twenty or more feedings an hour to supply them with enough aphids from the rose bushes, soft caterpillars from the trees, and other delicacies. They were also given the tender sprouts of plants.

After fourteen days in the nest, the two

biggest babies flew out of it. The next day the other three followed their example. Although they had had no practice, all of them could fly quite well. The young birds stayed near each other, while the parents worked hard to bring food enough to satisfy their begging brood.

By the end of two weeks the fledglings

had learned to find their own food. Their mother left them now, to start another family. But for a few days longer White Patch would still give an insistent youngster an extra tidbit—a Japanese beetle, perhaps, or a cabbage butterfly caught in the air.

Not long after the young birds had be-

come completely independent, White Patch and his mate were caring for another brood; and later they raised still another.

By the end of the summer there was a large flock of house sparrows in the garden. Many of them wandered away from their first home, as White Patch had done when he left Battery Park. But when winter came again, there was no lack of birds at the feeding table. Noticeable among them was White Patch, the city sparrow.

DATE DUE

HIGHSMITH 45-110